THERE WERE TWO TREES IN THE GARDEN
STUDY GUIDE

KAREN JEAN WILLIAMS

MorningStar Publications
A DIVISION OF MORNINGSTAR FELLOWSHIP CHURCH
375 Star Light Drive, Fort Mill, SC 29715
www.MorningStarMinistries.org

There Were Two Trees in the Garden Study Guide
by Karen Jean Williams
Copyright © 2008
International Standard Book Number— 978-1-59933-436-3

For use with:
There Were Two Trees in the Garden
by Rick Joyner
Copyright © 1985
Mass Market 2nd Printing, 2007
International Standard Book Number—978-1-929371-55-6

Distributed by MorningStar Publications, Inc.,
a division of MorningStar Fellowship Church,
375 Star Light Drive, Fort Mill, SC 29715
www.MorningStarMinistries.org
1-800-542-0278

Cover Design: Kevin Lepp
Book Layout: Dana Zondory

TABLE OF CONTENTS

INTRODUCTION

This study guide has been written for use with the book *There Were Two Trees in the Garden* by Rick Joyner. The purpose of this guide is to enable the reader to gain a deeper understanding of the teachings in the book. It is also designed to promote spiritual growth by encouraging readers to daily apply to their lives the biblical principles taught whenever possible.

This study guide may be completed individually, with others in a group, or in a classroom setting. Each chapter includes one memory verse. Additionally, there are parts of the guide marked "CHALLENGE" that encourage further study. These require a fair amount of biblical knowledge and are intended to be optional.

In his book, Rick helps us to better understand the impact that resulted in our lives from Adam's choice to eat of the fruit of the Tree of the Knowledge of Good and Evil. Rick teaches us many spiritual truths as he illuminates various Scriptures in Genesis and Exodus. These truths reveal some of the aspects of man's character that resulted from Adam's disastrous decision. He then helps us to glean the victory that Christ has established for us over our Adamic nature as he discusses the Passover.

As you read *There Were Two Trees in the Garden* and work through this study guide, you will gain a better understanding of the challenges these two eternally significant trees represent. You will also better understand yourself and some of the attitudes that you may struggle with. This study is intended to enable you to identify areas in your own life where the Tree of the Knowledge of Good and Evil is still rooted. Its purpose is to encourage you to partake more deeply of the Tree of Life in order to destroy self-centered roots and grow in Christ. Those who partake of this tree daily will be rewarded with an exciting, life-changing relationship with the living God. Eat liberally of the Tree of Life and be transformed.

Karen Jean Williams

CHAPTER ONE
THE TWO TREES

1. When God planted the Garden of Eden, He purposefully placed in it two trees bearing fruit with eternal significance. One tree represents Christ, who is our Life, and the other represents death, which is the result of the knowledge of self. Rick explains that the Tree of the Knowledge of Good and Evil is a biblical model of the Law (see page 8). Specifically, how does this knowledge bring death?

2. Prior to eating fruit from the Tree of Knowledge, Adam and Eve had not noticed their nakedness. At that time, where was their attention focused?

3. Adam and Eve's first response after partaking of the forbidden fruit was self-inspection. This was the result of the self-centeredness which had entered into them. Keeping our focus on the Lord can help free us from this malady. Can you think of several Scriptures that help you keep your focus on Jesus?

Choose one of these verses and memorize it this week.

4. On page 14, Rick states that when a man is born again, God "immediately begins to separate the light from the darkness in his life. In our zeal for Him, we may try to take over this work and perform it by the only way we have ever known—through the knowledge of good and evil. This struggle between law and grace—flesh and Spirit—is the source of inner discord afflicting most Christians." Only the Holy Spirit can change our hearts. Take a minute to consider whether or not you are in the midst of this struggle. If so, in what way are you striving to remove the darkness from within yourself?

5. Are you willing to release this work to the Holy Spirit?

If yes, then choose to trust that He will complete His good work in you (see Philippians 1:6).

6. On page 15, Rick discusses two spiritual lineages coming forth from two seeds. What are they and from where does each come?

7. **CHALLENGE:** In the first chapter, Rick states, "It was not *just* man's disobedience that brought death to the world, but the fruit from the tree" (see page 8). From reading the chapter and from your own biblical knowledge, describe several ways "fruit" has come forth from this tree. How has that fruit brought death to mankind?

NOTES

CHAPTER TWO
THE SEED OF CAIN

1. As a type of Adam, the seed of Cain is confined to the natural realm. Those who are of this seed are worshipers of the creation rather than the Creator. What are some of the ways that non-Christian, "religious" people worship creation?

2. Christians are of the seed of Christ, yet our transformation to Christ-likeness is a process.

    A. Can you think of any religious activities that Christians may participate in which are rooted in self-worship or "religion" rather than worship of the Creator?

    B. How has "religion" affected your life?

3. On page 22, Rick teaches that the man of sin is the personification of the sin of man. He points out that the mark of the beast is simply evidence of worshiping the spirit of the world. Rather than being concerned with what the mark may look like, we are to be focused on our relationship with Christ, our Deliverer.

   A. List several things of this world that some Christians may worship (give priority over the Lord).

   B. Consider the way you prioritize your time and activities. If you are struggling with priorities that are out of order, what will help you to change? See Zechariah 4:6 and Ephesians 3:20.

   C. Now describe what you do daily to focus on the Lord and know Him better. What would you like to do differently?

   Take a minute to pray for God's help with this.

4. On page 23, Rick states, "The nature of the beast is rooted just as much in the 'good' that is in man as it is in the evil . . . The 'good' of the Tree of Knowledge kills just as certainly as the evil." Good rooted in this tree is more deceptive than evil. Only that which comes from God is good (see Matthew 19:16-17).

   A. What good works do some people possibly do with the motivation of earning God's approval?

   Remember: "The good that is in man will never redeem him from the evil that is in him" (see page 26).

   B. How can we be sure our good works please God? See Romans 8:14.

5. To be deceived is to be misled by false words or appearance. Many Christians were deceived by the good works of Hitler in the early years of his leadership. On page 26, Rick states that "Satan is capable of using either good or evil as a tool to bring about his purposes." What can Christians do to protect themselves from deception?

6. **CHALLENGE:** Rick quotes Philippians 3:2-9 near the end of Chapter Two. In light of the teaching in this chapter, why did Paul consider all of his accomplishments prior to his salvation as loss?

CHAPTER THREE
THE SACRIFICE

1. In your own words, explain why Cain's offering of the fruit of the ground was rejected by God and why Abel's offering of the fat portions from the firstborn of his flock was accepted by God (see page 32 and Genesis 3:17-19, 4:2-5).

2. **CHALLENGE:** Rick teaches that we are not to resist personal injustices and cites Matthew 5:38-48. On page 35, he states, "There is a power in nonresistance to evil that crushes the serpent's head." This spiritual principle strongly conflicts with our natural thinking of dealing with evil. Explain why the principle is true.

3. Jesus came to save the world. Rick states, "He has commissioned us with that same purpose. If it is to be accomplished through us, we, too, must lay down our lives" (see page 37). How are you working this out in your own life?

4. On page 38, Rick points out that forgiveness is a requirement, not an option, citing Matthew 6:14-15.

   A. Why did God make it a requirement?

   B. Whom do you need to forgive? Will you do so now?

   C. In the past when you have been treated unjustly, how have you responded?

   D. How would you like to respond?

5. Read Galatians 2:20 in several different translations and spend some time meditating on it. Choose your favorite translation and memorize the verse this week.

6. Jesus laid aside His rights and chose the humiliation of the cross so that we could enjoy eternal life with Him. Read Philippians 2:5-9 in several different translations and meditate on it. Then write what God is speaking to you about these verses.

7. On page 39, Rick reminds us that Jesus gave us a new commandment to love one another as He has loved us. What are some things you can do to enable yourself to grow in this kind of love? See Psalm 27:8, John 15:4-8, and I John 3:16-18.

NOTES

CHAPTER FOUR
THE ROOT OF DOUBLE-MINDEDNESS

1. One who is double-minded has more than one mind or personality. This impacts in varying degrees all who are living in their carnal nature without Christ. What is the cause of double-mindedness, and what is the only solution to the problem?

2. In this same section, Rick explains that "one of the most dominating fears afflicting fallen man is the fear of rejection" (see page 42).

    A. Explain in your own words how this fear contributes to double-mindedness.

    B. List at least two things you can do to get free from the fear of man (see II Kings 18:5-6).

3. What advice did Sigmund Freud give to people, believing it would help them get free of guilt?

4. Briefly explain how Freud's advice has contributed to the great increase in lawlessness in our society over the last fifty years.

5. If you are struggling with practicing **"the very evil that I do not want" (see Romans 7:19)**, how can you overcome the struggle?

    •   Zechariah 4:6

    •   Romans 6:14

    •   I Corinthians 10:13

    •   Philippians 4:13

    Meditate on these verses this week. Also, choose one and memorize it.

6. In the section titled "The Onslaught of Humanism," Rick teaches that those who grew up without authoritarian guidelines became rebellious. Why will these be easily won over by a tyrant? See page 49.

7. In this same section, Rick states that Christians who draw close to the Lord "will become the most consistent, decisive, stable people the world has ever known." He goes on to say, "Those who truly know their God are the most confident, humble, and peaceful people on earth" (see page 49).

    A. List at least three verses that will help you to develop these Christ-like qualities.

B. In addition to meditating on Scripture, what else can you do to grow in these qualities? See Psalm 27:8 and 14.

8. **CHALLENGE:** Rick teaches that the distinguishing characteristics of true Christians are that they practice righteousness and love one another. We cannot focus on the law to accomplish this because we are not able to fulfill it and our sin-nature will consume us. He states, "Our 'practice of righteousness' is to abide in Him (Christ)." From the remainder of the chapter and Ezekiel 36:25-27, explain how abiding in the Lord enables us to develop these two characteristics.

CHAPTER FIVE
BABYLON

1. Selfish ambition was the source of man's true purpose to build a tower that reached heaven: **"let us make for ourselves" (see Genesis 11:4).** Explain briefly where this attitude came from and what ultimately results from it. See pages 55-56.

2. What two spirits are connected to Babel? See James 3:16.

3. In the section titled "The Root of Christian Disunity," Rick teaches that during the Middle Ages the Lord scattered the Christian church through denominations (languages).

   A. Why do you suppose this happened?

B. When can truth kill?

4. How can we be free from Babylon? See I John 1:7-9 and Colossians 3:12-17.

5. In the latter part of this same section, what weakness is found among those who contribute to division in the body of Christ?

6. How can one overcome this weakness? See Psalm 118:8 and John 15:13.

Select one of these two verses and memorize it this week.

7. What is the focal point of true unity?

8. When we examine teachings by the Word of God, what can help us to have a right motivation? See Psalm 51:10 and Ephesians 3:17.

9. In the section titled "True Unity," Rick urges us to restore those who need correction, citing Galatians 6:1. From your knowledge of Scripture, why is this important to the Lord? See also II Corinthians 5:18-21.

10. In the last section of the chapter, Rick teaches about the pride of the seed of Cain. He wrote, "The people of Babel actually believed that they could reach heaven by their own efforts. **'Let us build...let us make' (see Genesis 11:4).** This is an echo of the serpent's temptation of Eve—that she could become like God without God. Since the success of that temptation, Satan has been able to keep man devoted to this folly . . . he has always had one god—himself" (see page 63). There is only one true remedy for man's folly. Read Psalm 51 in several versions and meditate on it. Then write what the Lord is speaking to you.

CHAPTER SIX
THE ANTITHESIS TO BABYLON

1. Pentecost is the antithesis to Babylon. Rick teaches that the gift of tongues "is the language of God which penetrates all facades to touch the inner man" (see pages 65-66). Read Romans 8:26-27, and then explain this statement in your own words.

2. From the first section of this chapter, how will unity come to the body of Christ? See also John 17:20-23.

3. What can each of us do to help bring it about?

4. On pages 67-68, Rick states, "Jesus is the finished work of God. He was the beginning of the work of God and He is the end, the Alpha and Omega . . . Everything that God is doing is found in Christ...." For each of the verses listed below, describe the work(s) of God found in Christ.

- Matthew 5:17

- Romans 5:10

- John 14:9

- I John 1:9

- John 1:1-3

Now list some others and include Scripture references.

Choose one of the above verses and memorize it this week.

5. Although our intent is good, our efforts to become like Christ will always be rooted in the Tree of the Knowledge of Good and Evil. If we are not to *try* to be Christ-like, then how can we be conformed to His image? See Psalm 51:10 and Hebrews 4:15-16. Also read II Corinthians 12:7-10 in several versions and meditate on it.

6. **CHALLENGE:** Only through the Holy Spirit can we perceive Christ's spiritual nature. How is the resurrected Christ different than the "MAN from Galilee?"

NOTES

CHAPTER SEVEN
ABRAHAM

1. Rick states that Abraham "continually released everything to the Lord, trusting Him to accomplish all that concerned him" (see page 73). What do you need to release to the Lord today?

2. Spiritual vision is the ability to "look" at things with our hearts that the natural eye cannot see. It is getting God's perspective on a matter. As Rick states, when we have it, "space and time cease to limit our vision; the future becomes as real as the present" (see page 74). This vision enabled Abraham to obey God through the most difficult circumstances. In what areas of your life do you desire to have your spiritual vision increased?

Take a minute to pray and ask the Holy Spirit to do this for you. Also, ask the Lord to give you Scriptures that will help you get His perspective on your particular situation.

3. Throughout Chapter Seven, Rick teaches about true faith. In a couple of brief sentences, define true faith. See Psalm 9:10 and Isaiah 26:3.

4. Rick states, "Many of the doctrines that are called 'faith' today are the result of dangerous grasping by those who are still earthly-minded. In these cases, the thrust of the teaching will place a great deal of emphasis on earthly blessing and attainment" (see page 76). This kind of "faith" satisfies our fleshly desires for self-satisfaction and self-exaltation. Read James 3:14-17 and explain how we can discern the difference between true faith and that which is earthly-minded.

5. Paul demonstrated his faith when he was content in all circumstances. How can we achieve this in our own lives? See Isaiah 54:10, Psalm 56:3-4, and Acts 16:22-26.

6. In the latter part of the section titled "True Faith," Rick teaches that the promises of God were made to Christ so that we can be found in Him. These promises are to be fulfilled in our lives through Christ who is our inheritance. List several promises that you are holding onto in your present circumstances. Be sure to include Scripture references.

Now select one of those Scriptures to memorize this week.

7. **CHALLENGE:** From the section titled "The Great Separation": In light of the "two trees" in the Garden of Eden, why do you think Jesus established that God's work for us is to **"believe in Him whom He has sent?" (see John 6:29)**

8. In the section titled "Faith and Patience," we learn that "true faith cannot be separated from patience" (see Hebrews 6:12). How do we grow in patience? See James 1:2-4 and Romans 15:5.

Remember that Christ-likeness is a process. Growing in patience takes time (and patience).

9. In the same section, Rick states, "If we are seeking true faith, we must allow ourselves to be carried well beyond the limits of human ability" (see page 84). In what way does the Lord want to stretch your faith?

10. In the final section of Chapter Seven, Rick teaches that Ishmael and all the problems he brought to Abraham's family (and his descendants) were the result of Abraham's impatience. He sought to bring forth the promises of God himself rather than wait for the Lord's timing. How can we determine if our actions are sowing seeds of the flesh or of the Spirit? See Psalm 139:23-24.

CHAPTER EIGHT
LOOKING FOR A CITY

1. According to Hebrews 11:10, Abraham was looking for a city that had foundations. What were the foundations he found? See Genesis 15:1 and John 8:56, 58.

2. In the section titled "Spiritual Foundations," Rick tells us that as a young Christian he built his foundation on the revelation of the church.

    A. What sign did God give to Rick that indicated his foundation was faulty?

    B. In what areas of your life are you struggling with faulty foundations?

3. In this same section, we are admonished to build deep foundations before building up. After each of the following Scripture references, write how one builds down in Christ.

    •   Psalm 119:11, 93

- Matthew 6:33

- Hebrews 10:23-25

4. **CHALLENGE:** Rick states: "We must see everything through [Christ]. When we try to see Him through the lens of our own doctrines, our view of Him will be distorted" (see page 93). How can we avoid understanding Jesus through our interpretation of Scripture, rather than interpreting Scripture through our understanding of Jesus?

5. Rick instructs us: "When taught as isolated extremes, even the greatest spiritual truths will leave the church in fragments" (see page 93).

   A. How can this happen?

   B. How can it be avoided?

6. We can seek God's truths yet still be deceived by the enemy. Briefly explain how this might happen.

7. List at least two admonishments Rick gives to leaders in the last portion of the section titled "Spiritual Foundations."

8. John the Baptist successfully achieved his God-given mission which was to reveal the Messiah. Read Luke 3:1-22 and John 1:6-8, 19-34. List the ways that John accomplished this.

9. According to the last two paragraphs of Chapter Eight, what two missions are we to accomplish?

10. Select a verse from this lesson and meditate on it this week, and then memorize it.

NOTES

CHAPTER NINE
JACOB AND ESAU, REUBEN AND JOSEPH

1. Rick indicates that many Christians thoughtlessly exchange their birthright in Christ for temporary, carnal gratification (see pages 99-100). In an effort to help us understand the significance of this, he states, "The Lord Jesus purchased with His own blood the opportunity for us to come boldly before the very throne of God." Using the following Scriptures, describe what Christ accomplished for us.

   • Ephesians 2:1-7

   • Hebrews 9:14-15, 26

   • Hebrews 10:19-22

2. In the section titled "Wrestling with God," we read of Jacob's determination to obtain his spiritual inheritance, even to the point of being willing to risk his life for it.

   A. After each Scripture reference write what your spiritual inheritance is in Christ.

   • Genesis 15:1

- Matthew 19:29

- Matthew 25:34

- Hebrews 6:11-12

- Revelation 21:7

Select one of the above verses to meditate upon and memorize this week.

B. How will you contend for your inheritance?

3. The carnal nature of men is food for Satan because it empowers him by giving him access to operate through them. The enemy deceptively invites people, including Christians, to worship him through their flesh. Rick states that this "is usually simply an invitation to take the wider, more traveled path" (see page 103).

A. Other than Esau and Reuben, can you think of a few people in Scripture who chose immediate gratification rather than wrestle with God for their inheritance?

B. What was the result of their fleshly choices?

C. How did Jesus overcome temptation? See Luke 4.

4. In light of Rick's comment that "carnal men respond to carnal strength" (see page 103), how can we overcome the temptation to follow leaders according to their outward appearances? See John 16:13 and Acts 4:13.

5. The Lord "does not call us for our strengths—He calls us for our weaknesses. Just as our Lord Jesus emptied Himself to become a servant, He looks for those who will have no confidence in the flesh and will become vessels for His Spirit" (see page 106). In light of this, what do you have to offer God?

6. In the last section of Chapter Eight, Rick discusses "Body, Soul, and Spirit." He quotes Romans 8:14: **"For all who are being led by the Spirit of God, these are sons of God."** What are the signs in your life that you are led by the Holy Spirit?

- Body:

- Soul:

- Spirit:

Pray over your answers and ask the Holy Spirit to help you grow in needed areas.

CHAPTER TEN
PHARAOH, MOSES, AND SPIRITUAL AUTHORITY

1. Rick teaches that Moses' character is "a wonderful example of the self-sacrificing nature of true spiritual authority, as opposed to the self-seeking nature of human authority" (see page 112). From your knowledge of Scripture, list at least three things Moses did that demonstrated true spiritual authority.

2. **CHALLENGE:** When we choose to follow Christ, He becomes our Master, yet we actually experience liberty. **"So if the Son sets you free, you will be free indeed"** (**John 8:36** NIV). Explain why this paradox is true.

3. When discussing sexual bondage, Rick teaches that "every evil is the perversion of a God-given gift that is caused by man's attempt to find fulfillment and security outside of Christ. This only leads to dissatisfaction and insecurity" (see page 114).

   A. Apart from sexual immorality, what are some other ways people seek to find fulfillment outside of Christ?

   B. Insecurities are rooted in seeking satisfaction apart from the Lord. In what areas do you experience insecurity?

   C. Meditate on the following verses, then explain how you might overcome insecurities in your life: Psalm 36:5-9; John 10:27-29; Deuteronomy 33:12.

4. Rick states that the "fear of rejection is probably the most dominant force within those who have not been 'crucified with Christ'" (see page 115). How is the fear of rejection connected to the Tree of the Knowledge of Good and Evil?

5. Christ's perfect love for us casts out fear (see I John 4:18). It is His wonderful solution to overcoming every kind of fear, including the fear of rejection. After each Scripture reference, write how Christians can grow in their ability to receive the Lord's perfect love and overcome fear.

   • Proverbs 29:25

   • Isaiah 26:3

   • Psalm 63:3-7

6. **"Everyone must submit himself to the governing authorities, for there is no authority except that which God has established. The authorities that exist have been established by God"** (**Romans 13:1 NIV**). In order to exercise true spiritual authority, we must submit to our nation's leaders whether or not we agree with them. David provided us with an example of this when he recognized that although King Saul had become corrupt, he was appointed by God and was to be honored as long as he remained Israel's leader. Read I Samuel 26:1-11, and then answer the following questions.

   A. What mistake do some Christians in our society make when they disagree with political leaders?

   B. What can we do for our leaders that would most please the Lord?

7. Humility is one of the key qualities of Christ's character that enabled Him to sacrifice Himself for us. It qualified Him to become the Head of the church. Meditate on Philippians 2:5-10.

    A. What is the Lord teaching you about leadership through this passage?

    B. What are you learning about leadership through Chapter Ten of *Two Trees*?

8. Rick states, "It has become very easy for a believer to be rightly related to the body . . . and have almost no relationship with the Lord. To be rightly related to the Lord is the most important element in every life and ministry" (page 126). Take a few minutes to consider how you spend your time each day.

    A. Is having time alone with Christ your top priority on a daily basis?

    B. What can you do to improve in this area?

9. In the section titled "Knowing God's Ways," Rick teaches that "Israel was called to be a nation of priests, to serve Him and manifest to all the peoples of the earth the character of her Creator" (see Exodus 19:5-6 and page 128 in *Two Trees*). As children of God, we have been adopted by Him and are now part of the royal priesthood in the Lord's holy nation (see I Peter 2:9).

    A. How can you fulfill this call?

B. According to Rick's teaching, what should we avoid doing as priests of the Lord?

10. **CHALLENGE:** For a mature leader to be developed by God, there are usually many years between the call of God and the commissioning to enter the ministry. How many years did God take to prepare the following leaders from the time of their call to the actual commencement of their ministry?

- Moses

- Joshua

- David

- Paul

11. Choose one of the verses from this lesson and memorize it this week.

NOTES

CHAPTER ELEVEN
THE FEAR OF GOD VS. THE FEAR OF MAN

1. King Saul clearly ruled Israel through his desire to please the people rather than the Lord. Yet David lived his life to please God. After receiving the anointing from Samuel but before he was crowned King of Israel, he experienced great trials and tests. From your knowledge of Scripture, list several "opportunities" David had to demonstrate that he feared the Lord more than man.

2. **CHALLENGE:** In the section titled "Saul and David," Rick teaches that sorcery is a work of the flesh (see Galatians 5:20) and describes it as "using any spirit or device to dominate, control, or manipulate another person or situation" (see page 138). Other than King Saul, name at least two people in Scripture who practiced this. Very briefly write what each one did and how it impacted his/her life.

3. At the end of this same section, Rick states, "We are to love the world with Christ's love, but we are not to be its friend" (see page 140).

    A. What does it mean to be a "friend of the world?"

    B. How do Christians demonstrate God's love to the world while avoiding friendship with it?

4. In the section titled "Satan's Basic Strategy," Rick teaches that there are four key tactics the enemy uses to defeat Christians. Read the Scripture references next to each of the strategies, and then write how you may overcome these attacks.

    A. DISCOURAGEMENT: II Corinthians 1:20; Romans 4:19-22

    B. DISORIENTATION: Ephesians 1:17-23

    C. LOSS OF VISION: Jeremiah 29:11; I Peter 2:9-10

    D. COMPROMISING: I Corinthians 9:24-27

    Choose one of the above verses and memorize it this week.

5. In this same section, Rick states, "Compromise has robbed the church of its power" (see page 140). He teaches that Satan knew that if during the Israelites' efforts to get free from bondage they "compromised to any degree at all, he would ultimately regain dominion over them" (see page 142). Take a few minutes to consider your own life.

A. In what areas would you like more freedom?

B. How have you compromised and therefore undermined your victory? (Ask the Holy Spirit to reveal truth to you in this.)

NOTES

CHAPTER TWELVE
THE PASSOVER

1. In Chapter Twelve, Rick reiterates his point from Chapter Two "that the good side of the Tree of Knowledge is just as deadly as the evil side and far more deceptive. Human goodness is an affront to the cross and is used as a compensation for it" (see page 146). How can we discern the difference between good works rooted in the Tree of Knowledge and good works that please God? See Romans 8:14; Ephesians 2:1-3; Philippians 2:13.

2. We are to have a "living relationship" with God.

    A. Briefly describe a "living relationship."

    B. How can we develop this kind of relationship with the Lord? Give Scripture references.

3. If we love the God of Truth more than the truths of God, we will be protected from deception and our doctrines will be rightly aligned with His Word. Ask the Holy Spirit to help you identify any truths/doctrines that you might love more than the Lord. Are you in pursuit of seeing a truth/doctrine established more than you are in pursuit of knowing Jesus Christ?

4. **CHALLENGE:** Read II Corinthians 5:17 in a couple of versions and meditate on it. Explain the spiritual change that takes place when one is born of God's Spirit and why Paul states Christians are a **"new creation"** (NIV).

5. Without Christ, man's world is very self-focused. In the section titled "A New Beginning," Rick states that "as we begin to see the kingdom of God, our perspective is changed. The more clearly we see Him sitting on His throne, the less we notice the combined problems and cares of the world." Later he quotes Ephesians 1:19-23.

    A. Describe Christ's position and authority according to this passage.

B. How does this truth change your perspective of your personal struggles and concerns?

C. In light of this, what should you be worried about?

6. If you could physically see Jesus with you all day long, everywhere you went, how would it impact your day? What would you do differently?

7. In the section titled "Walking in the Spirit," Rick teaches that "to walk in the Spirit is to see with His eyes, hear with His ears, and understand with His heart" (see page 152). In this state, we see the natural reality of what is happening on earth, but our response is rooted in God's perspective. After each of the following verses, write how we develop this kind of spiritual sight.

• Joshua 1:8

• II Corinthians 5:7

• Psalm 145:1-7

8. **CHALLENGE:** In this same section, we learn that the entire purpose of God for our lives is accomplished "when we have our whole being summed up in Him by simply abiding" (see page 154). Meditate on the following Scripture verses and then briefly explain this truth in your own words. If necessary, use a couple of different versions: John 6:29; Ephesians 3:17-19; Colossians 2:9-10.

9. In the section titled "Changing the Heart," judging ourselves and our motives are discussed. "Our judgment of ourselves will be distorted if it is not done by the Spirit" (see page 156). Using the following verses, outline the steps that enable a Christian to change and become more like Christ.

    *   Psalm 139:23-24

    *   I John 1:8-9

    *   II Corinthians 12:9

10. When we have been convicted of sin by the Holy Spirit and we have repented, where should our focus be?

11. Repentance and willingness to change does not prevent us from being tempted by the enemy. Jesus was tempted in all ways but was without sin. What enables us to overcome temptation? See I Corinthians 10:13 and Hebrews 4:14-16.

12. Like Christ, it is also important that we *choose* not to give in to temptation. Meditate on Hebrews 10:35-39, and then summarize it in your own words.

13. In Chapter Three of this study, you were asked to meditate on Galatians 2:20 and memorize it. Review the verse and meditate on it once again.

   A. Explain what it means to you in light of this chapter.

   B. As you have studied this chapter, in what areas has the Holy Spirit been dealing with you? How will you respond?

14. Choose a verse from this lesson and memorize it this week.

NOTES

CHAPTER THIRTEEN
TAKING THE LAMB INTO THE HOUSE

1. Many Christians believe that they must seek God's acceptance through their behavior. They do not understand that God's ways are higher than our ways, and we are only acceptable to the Father because Christ endured the cross for us. Why do you think many struggle with this?

2. Read Romans 5:6-11 in several translations and meditate upon it.

    A. Based on these verses, is it possible to earn God's acceptance?

    B. Explain the meaning of this passage in your own words.

3. Rick states that modern evangelism efforts are only resulting in a small percentage of true conversions (see pages 162-163). In light of this chapter, what can you do to help someone come to know Christ and experience true conversion?

4. List four Scripture references that will help you introduce Jesus Christ to an unbeliever. Keep in mind that they probably know very little about the character of God.

5. Who do you say Jesus is? Support your answer with Scripture references.

CHAPTER FOURTEEN
HE WAS CRUCIFIED BY US

1. In the section titled "Criticizing God," we are instructed that judging others is in effect saying that the Lord's workmanship in that individual does not meet our standards. Why is this true? Use Scriptures to support your answer.

2. Sometimes God has us in circumstances that are challenging for us, and sometimes we are in the wrong situation (i.e. we chose a job that was not God's will for us). How can we determine if our trial is God's plan for us or if we need to make a change? See Proverbs 3:5-6.

3. Read Isaiah 58:9-12 and meditate on it. List the promises God makes in these verses to those who stop criticizing and judging others.

4. Read Matthew 7:1-2, and then ask the Holy Spirit to reveal to you if you are judging others. If so, how will *you* be judged according to this Scripture passage?

5. According to Matthew 18:15-17, what are the steps we are to take when a brother or sister in Christ sins against us?

6. What is the ultimate goal of correction within the body of Christ? See Psalm 51:10-12, II Corinthians 5:18, and Galatians 6:1.

7. What is God's priority that He even places above our sacrifices and gifts to Him? See Matthew 5:23-24.

8. Is there someone whom you need to go to and make things right? If so, will you plan to do it quickly?

9. In the beginning of the section titled "Becoming God's Spokesman," Rick quotes Jeremiah 15:19. Read this verse in several versions.

   A. Explain what it means to **"extract the precious from the worthless"** (see **Jeremiah 15:19**) with regard to Christians.

   B. Give several specific examples of how you can do this with someone in your life.

NOTES

CHAPTER FIFTEEN
THE LIFE IS IN THE BLOOD

1. In the first section of Chapter Fifteen, we are confronted with the truth that knowledge of Christ's sacrifice for us is not enough to provide salvation. His life must be applied to our lives. From your knowledge of Scripture, explain this statement giving verse references.

2. In the section titled "The Increase of Knowledge," we are taught that "salvation is more than just forgiveness of sinful actions; it is deliverance from the indwelling evil that causes those actions! The crucifixion of Jesus accomplished an exchange for us—our body of death for His resurrection life . . . we must die to our lives, interests, and will to partake of Him" (see page 181). Read and meditate on Romans 6. Read it in several versions if needed.

   A. Write what the Lord is speaking to you through this passage.

B. **CHALLENGE:** Now summarize Romans 6 in a few sentences as though you were explaining it to a new Christian.

3. In John 6, Jesus taught that we must partake of His flesh and drink His blood to have eternal life. Just as the Lord provided food for the Israelites in the desert, Christ is the true Manna that came down from heaven, and we must partake of Him daily to receive fresh spiritual nourishment.

    A. List at least three ways we can gather fresh manna each day.

    B. What are you doing daily to receive spiritual nourishment? Be specific.

4. Read I Corinthians 11:23-30 in a couple of versions. In light of this Scripture passage and the *Two Trees* chapter, explain why Paul stated that many Corinthians were weak, sick, and sleeping (dead).

5. In Matthew 28:20, Jesus tells us that we are to observe all that He commanded. Rick teaches that "when we come with preconditions of which of His commandments we will accept, we void the very power of the gospel. Often, that which represents the greatest threat to us is what we need the most" (see page 187).

A. Pray and ask the Holy Spirit to help you see if there are commands from the Lord that you find difficult to follow. If so, write them down.

B. How can you overcome in these areas and obey the Lord? See Psalm 25:9 and James 4:6-7.

6. Rick also states that "true salvation is the deliverance from self-will and our self-life in exchange for His life" (see page 187). Spiritual maturity is a process worked in us by God's Holy Spirit.

A. What are some of the signs in a person's life that you believe indicate he/she has been delivered from self-will?

B. What can help set you free from self-will? Read:

• I John 1:9

- Psalm 51:17

- John 14:15

Memorize one of the above verses this week.

7. **CHALLENGE**: In the section titled "We Must Eat the Whole Thing," Rick teaches that Jesus is the sum of God's Word (see page 190). Briefly explain this statement. See John 1:1-4; Hebrews 1:2-3.

CHAPTER SIXTEEN
THE SPIRIT IS MOVING

1. In the first section of Chapter Sixteen titled "We Must Eat in Haste," we learn that leaven is symbolic of legalistic doctrine. Some Pharisees who had been saved through faith in Christ sought to force the Gentile believers to follow the Law of Moses and be circumcised. Read Acts 15:1-29.

   A. From verses 28-29, list the requirements the apostles gave to the Gentile believers after much deliberation.

   B. Why do you suppose they did not tell the Gentile believers to follow the Ten Commandments that God gave to Moses on Mt. Sinai? See Galatians 2:16; 5:1-6 and Matthew 22:37-40.

2. In this same section, Rick teaches that "doctrines that disturb and unsettle the body of Christ are often rooted in legalism. There is a continual pressure upon the church to walk in principles and/or formulas to gain maturity. These doctrines usually seem **'good for food . . . a delight to the eyes, and . . . desirable to make one wise'"** (**Genesis 3:6** and see page 195).

    A. Can you think of doctrines taught in the body of Christ that are unsettling by pressuring Christians or cause division?

    B. Read Ezekiel 36:25-27. Who has responsibility for our Christian maturity?

    C. What is our part in becoming Christ-like?

- Proverbs 28:13 and I John 1:9

- Mark 9:23

- Mark 12:28-30

3. In the section titled "A Righteousness Greater Than the Law," we learn that if we walk by the Spirit we will actually go beyond obedience to the Law and we will fulfill it. It is the love of God poured into our hearts by the Holy Spirit that enables us to live in a righteousness that is greater than the Law. Read Ezekiel 36:25-27 again and then read Romans 5:5 and John 14:15 (NIV or NASB).

    A. According to these verses, what enables us to obey the Lord?

    B. **CHALLENGE:** Briefly explain in your own words why obedience out of love is a righteousness greater than obedience to the Law.

4. Why is it easier for Christians to follow rules (legalism) than to be led of the Spirit? Support your answer with Scriptures.

5. In the section titled "Spiritual Order," Rick explains that the body of Christ must be guided by its Head rather than lots of regulations. When we try to resolve problems in the church with new rules, what is the result? What is a better way to handle problems?

6. In this same section, Rick teaches that "there is no true rest in the law until there is death—making men machines or zombies instead of humans who are able to have a relationship with their Creator" (see page 199). Using this chapter and the following verses, explain why the Law brings death, and life is only found in Christ. See Galatians 2:16, 21; 3:10-12, 19-25.

7. Select one verse from this lesson and memorize it this week.

CHAPTER SEVENTEEN
NO STRANGER MAY EAT OF IT

1. In the beginning of Chapter Seventeen, Rick teaches that church leaders must be careful not to allow the unconverted who attend services to become members of the church body. How can we discern who has been born of God's Spirit? Use Scripture references to support your answer.

2. In the section titled "Vain Worship," we learn about those who attend church and appear to be believers by saying the right things, behaving correctly, and even believing Christian doctrines. Yet Jesus was clear in His conversation with Nicodemus that one must be born of God's Spirit (see John 3:1-6). In his letter to the Corinthians, the Apostle Paul explained that when the new birth takes place, we become a new creation in Jesus Christ (see II Corinthians 5:17). This is the result of a conversion experience. Have you had a specific experience where you knew that you were born of God's Spirit, becoming a new creation in Christ? If so, briefly write about it. If not, will you now acknowledge your desperate need for this new birth through faith in Jesus Christ? Will you pray and ask the Lord to forgive you for your sins and believe that the sacrifice of Jesus' blood was provided for your forgiveness?

3. In the section titled "The Habitation of God," Rick compares the Outer Court, the Holy Place, and the Holy of Holies in the Tabernacle of Moses to three types of ministry. Explain each type in your own words.

- Outer Court:

- Holy Place:

- Holy of Holies:

4. Take a few minutes to consider how you spend time each day/week. How are you ministering in each area?

- Outer Court:

- Holy Place:

- Holy of Holies:

5. Many Christians are consumed with Outer Court ministry but miss the joys of the Most Holy Place (see Psalm 42:7-8; Zephaniah 3:17). What changes would you like to see take place in the time you spend in the Most Holy Place?

Now ask the Holy Spirit to help you change so that He may bring forth the Father's purposes for your intimate time with Him.

6. Memorize Zephaniah 3:17 this week.

7. In the final section of this chapter, "The Reason for the Tares," Rick discusses the need to allow the Lord to sort out the wheat and tares in our churches. In your own words, briefly explain why we must allow both wheat and tares to grow together and trust the Father to properly sort them in the end.

NOTES

CHAPTER EIGHTEEN
THE VICTORY

1. In the first section of this chapter, Rick discusses the material provision the Lord gave to the Israelites just prior to leaving Egypt. When the Lord chooses to bless His children with material wealth, what might be His purposes? Use Scripture to support your answer.

2. The reason many Christians continue in the carnal pursuit of earthly treasures is because they have not truly seen Christ as He is. Read each Scripture below and describe the Lord as He is.

   • Psalm 24:7-10

   • John 1:3

   • Ephesians 1:18-23

- Ephesians 3:20

- Hebrews 1:1-4

- Revelation 1:12-18

- Revelation 19:11-16

Now take a minute to pray and ask the Holy Spirit to increase your revelation and understanding of who Christ is.

3. Some Christians believe we are to abound in worldly wealth and others believe we are to live abased.

   A. According to this chapter, what is the correct objective for our lives?

   B. Read Philippians 4:11-13. What is the Lord's desire for us in this matter?

C. When we pursue wealth, where have we placed our trust?

4. In this section, Rick quotes Hebrews 11:35-40 and teaches that those who sought a better resurrection (a greater inheritance in Christ) willingly suffered persecution for their Lord, rather than focus on empty, worldly treasures. Read and meditate on this passage as well as Luke 9:23 and Galatians 2:20. What is the Lord saying to you about this truth?

5. Rick states that "the truly spiritual man is thus because his heart is so captured by the things of the spirit that he simply has no time or interest for the things of the world . . . Those who still have a love for worldly pleasures simply have not received the love of the Father" (see page 217). After each of the following verses, describe the Father's heart.

   • Exodus 34:5-7

   • Jeremiah 31:3

- John 3:16-17

- I John 3:1

6. In the section titled "The Waving of the Sheaf," we learn that the location of Abraham's burial tomb was of great importance to him, as well as Isaac, Jacob, and Joseph so they could be part of the first resurrection. What one character quality of Abraham truly pleased God? See Romans 4:13-22 and Hebrews 11:6.

Congratulations! You have just completed eighteen lessons designed to enable you to better understand the impact Adam's decision to eat of the Tree of the Knowledge of Good and Evil has had on your life, and to empower you to overcome sin through the victory gleaned by partaking of Jesus Christ, the Tree of Life. Take joy in partaking of Him daily because **"His divine power has granted to us everything pertaining to life and godliness, through the true knowledge of Him who called us by His own glory and excellence"** (see II Peter 1:3).

ADDITIONAL STUDY GUIDES
BY MORNINGSTAR

The Overcoming Life is about the ultimate quest of the true Christian life— how to become like the Lord and do the works that He did. True Christianity is not a life of working, but of becoming. It is the pursuit of seeing the glory of the Lord and being changed by that glory into His same image.

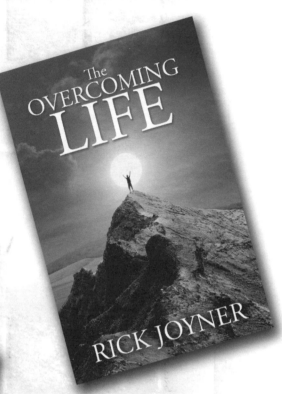

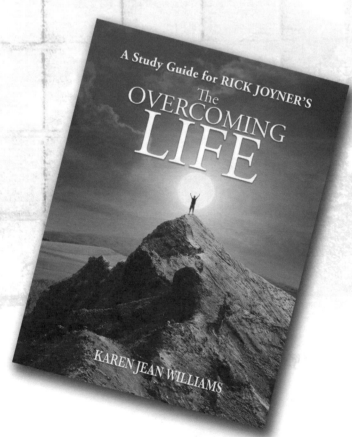

This study guide is intended to highlight and fortify the crucial revelation found in **The Overcoming Life** by Rick Joyner

🌙 MorningStar
PC Study Bible

"We believe this is the most powerful, easy to use Bible and Christian Research program available, and it would be a value at several times this price."
—Rick Joyner

Premium Edition

BIBLESOFT

PC STUDY BIBLE
MORNINGSTAR MINISTRIES

"I have been using this Bible program for more than ten years. I think it is the best, easiest to use, and contains the most tools and resources of any that I've seen. We are very excited to include many of our books and resources in this remarkable product."

PREMIUM EDITION

A LA CARTE VALUE OF $2,200

Our Price $159.00

Retail $199.00 You Save $40.00

Additional Copies $99.00
You Save $100.00

Includes all of the books in the Standard Edition PLUS:

- Several additional Bible translations and commentaries
- Over 50 books from church history
- Also includes: *The Final Quest Series, The Overcoming Series,* and more!

Standard Edition

BIBLESOFT

PC STUDY BIBLE
MORNINGSTAR MINISTRIES

"I have been using this Bible program for more than ten years. I think it is the best, easiest to use, and contains the most tools and resources of any that I've seen. We are very excited to include many of our books and resources in this remarkable product."

STANDARD EDITION

A LA CARTE VALUE OF $860

Our Price $79.00

Retail $99.00 You Save $20.00

Additional Copies $49.00
You Save $50.00

Includes:

- Multiple Bible Translations
- Complete Bible Commentary
- Bible History Collection
- Maps, Photos, & Much More
- PLUS: Nine of MorningStar's Books

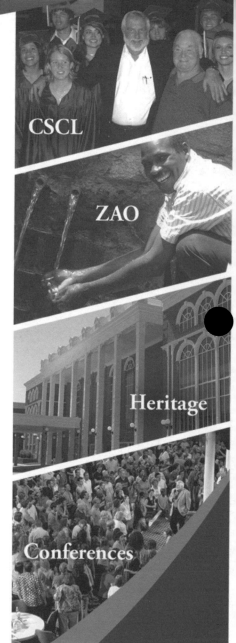

VISIT
www.MorningStarMinistries.org

Be Here Even When
You Can't Be Here

- View Revival Updates, Video Words for the Day, and Highlight Videos
- Read Rick's Word for the Day and Other Timely Articles
- View Upcoming Conferences and Events
- Webstream all MorningStar Services
- VISIT THE ONLINE STORE

HERITAGE INTERNATIONAL MINISTRIES

CONFERENCE & RETREAT CENTER

After extensive renovations, The Heritage Grand Hotel and Conference Center is once again becoming one of the premier gathering places for Christians from around the world. One television news reporter called it "a resurrection," and it has already become a symbol of the power of restoration and redemption.

Whether you are hosting a conference for two thousand, a seminar for two dozen, a wedding, leadership team meeting, or benefit luncheon, Heritage offers venues of different sizes, and a full array of services to assist you in hosting a successful event. Our facilities feature more than 50,000 square feet of flexible meeting space, including our 10,000 square foot Grand Ballroom and our 10,000 square foot Atrium Sanctuary.

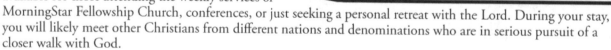

Over 360 rooms, suites, and apartments are now available for those attending the weekly services of MorningStar Fellowship Church, conferences, or just seeking a personal retreat with the Lord. During your stay, you will likely meet other Christians from different nations and denominations who are in serious pursuit of a closer walk with God.

All of our rates are set to be the best available for comparable facilities and service anywhere. Special rates are available for extended stays and for groups. The comfortable atmosphere is especially conducive to study, writing, prayer, worship, and fellowship.

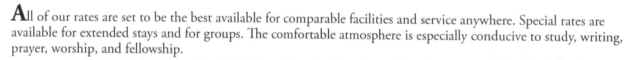

For reservations and information,
call 1-800-542-0278,
visit us online at: www.MorningStarMinistries.org, or
write to us at 375 Star Light Drive, Fort Mill, SC 29715